Hodder Gibson

Scottish Examination Materials

INTERMEDIATE 2

MATHS
Practice Papers

Peter W. Westwood

HODDER
GIBSON
PART OF HACHETTE LIVRE UK

Hachette's policy is to use papers that are natural, renewable and recyclable products and made from wood grown in sustainable forests. The logging and manufacturing processes are expected to conform to the environmental regulations of the country of origin.

Orders: please contact Bookprint Ltd, 130 Milton Park, Abingdon, Oxon OX14 4SB. Telephone: (44) 01235 827720. Fax: (44) 01235 400454. Lines are open from 9.00–5.00, Monday to Saturday, with a 24 hour message answering service. You can also order through our website www.hoddereducation.co.uk.

British Library Cataloguing in Publication Data

A catalogue record for this title is available from the British Library.

ISBN-13: 978-0-340-81208-2

Published by Hodder Gibson, 2a Christie Street. Paisley PA1 1NB.
Tel: 0141 848 1609; Fax: 0141 889 6315; Email: hoddergibson@hodder.co.uk
First Published 2003
Impression number   10 9 8 7 6 5 4
Year   2009   2008

Typeset by Fakenham Photosetting Limited, Fakenham, Norfolk.
Printed by Martins The Printers, Berwick-upon-Tweed for Hodder Gibson, 2a Christie Street, Paisley, PA1 1NB, Scotland, UK

CONTENTS

PREFACE

Intermediate 2 Mathematics Practice Papers is suitable for all candidates at Intermediate 2, both those taking units 1, 2 and 3, and those taking units 1, 2 and Applications of Mathematics.

In the final exam there are two totally separate question papers:
- One for units 1, 2 and 3
- Another for units 1, 2 and Applications of Mathematics.

In the interests of economy of space, the layout of these practice papers differs from this.
- The formulae list, which is at the front of each SQA paper, is given on page 4 and not repeated.
- The questions for unit 3 have been coded M to indicate mathematics unit 3.
- The questions for the Applications of Mathematics unit have been coded A to indicate Applications of Mathematics.

Candidates studying unit 3 should omit all the A questions, and those doing the Applications of Mathematics unit should omit all the M questions. The questions to be omitted by each group are also listed at the start of each paper. These coded questions have been slotted in among those for units 1 and 2 in order to provide a reasonable gradation of difficulty for all candidates. If at the end of the day you find the final exam slightly easier than these papers, it could be because of all the effort you have spent in practice. Good luck with your exam.

Intermediate 2
Mathematics
Paper 1 – Non-calculator

PRACTICE PAPER A

NATIONAL
QUALIFICATIONS
Time: 45 minutes

You may *NOT* use a calculator.

**Candidates doing units 1, 2 and 3 should omit questions 5A, 9A.
Candidates doing units 1, 2 and Applications of Mathematics should omit
questions 4M, 7M, 8M.**

Marks

1 (*a*) Write down the gradient of the straight line with equation $2y = 4x + 5$. **(1)**

(*b*) Find the equation of the straight line shown in this diagram.

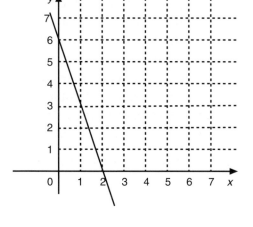

(3)

2 A group of pupils scored the following marks in a spelling test.

  8   7   5   9   7   6   7   8   5   9

(*a*) Construct a frequency table for this data and add a cumulative frequency column. **(2)**

(*b*) Calculate the probability that a pupil chosen at random from this group scored higher than 7. **(1)**

3   In this diagram:
   - TN is the tangent at A to the circle with centre C.
   - DN passes through C.
   - AĈN = 40°.
   - CT̂N = 25°.

   Showing all your working, calculate the size of DĈT.

Marks

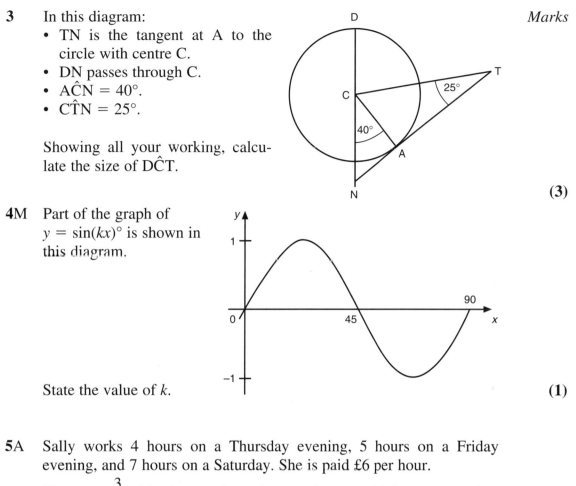

(3)

4M   Part of the graph of $y = \sin(kx)°$ is shown in this diagram.

   State the value of k.

(1)

5A   Sally works 4 hours on a Thursday evening, 5 hours on a Friday evening, and 7 hours on a Saturday. She is paid £6 per hour.

   She saves $\dfrac{3}{8}$ of her pay each week towards a new hi-fi system costing £480.

   How many weeks will she need to save to be able to afford the hi-fi system?

(5)

6   Some nails are sold in packets of 50. A sample of 11 packets contained the following numbers of nails.

   52   58   56   55   48   56   58   50   57   49   51

   (*a*)   For the above data, find the median and the upper and lower quartiles.

(3)

7

Marks

(*b*) Does this data support the manufacturer's claim that 'there are 50 nails on average per packet'?

(1)

(*c*) Construct a box plot for this data.

(2)

(*d*) For a different size of nail, also sold in packets of 50, another sample of packets was taken and the box plot for this sample is shown below.

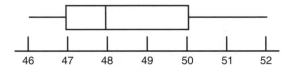

Is this manufacturer putting an appropriate number of these nails in each packet? Give a reason for your answer.

(1)

7M This diagram shows the graph of $y = 8 - kx^2$.

Find the value of k.

(2)

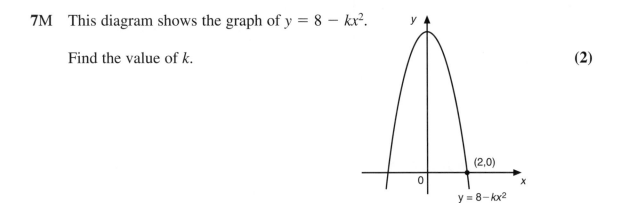

8M (*a*) Simplify $\dfrac{x^{\frac{3}{2}} \times x^{\frac{5}{2}}}{x}$.

(2)

(*b*) Express $\dfrac{5}{\sqrt{7}}$ with a rational denominator.

(2)

(*c*) Express $\dfrac{4}{x} + \dfrac{3}{x + 2}$ as a single fraction in its simplest form.

(3)

Marks

9A A chiropractor uses the flowchart below to determine her total charge on completion of treatment of a patient using medical insurance.

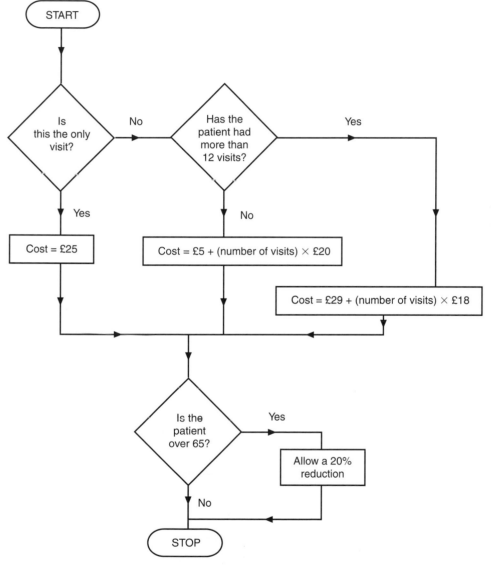

Calculate the cost of a series of 15 visits by a 72-year old man.   **(5)**

Total: 37 marks

[END OF QUESTION PAPER]

Intermediate 2
Mathematics
Paper 2

PRACTICE PAPER A

NATIONAL
QUALIFICATIONS
Time: 1 hour 30 minutes

Calculators may be used in this paper.

**Candidates doing units 1, 2 and 3 should omit questions 8A, 14A, 16A.
Candidates doing units 1, 2 and Applications of Mathematics should omit
questions 7M, 11M, 13M, 17M.**

Marks

1   A girl sent out eight thank-you letters after receiving birthday presents.
     She counted the number of words in each letter and obtained the results
     below.

     102   89   94   102   95   108   111   99

     Use an appropriate formula to calculate the standard deviation, showing
     all your working clearly.   **(4)**

2   Expand and simplify $(x + 3)(x^2 - 2x + 1)$.   **(3)**

3   Factorise   (*a*) $p^2 - 3p$.   **(1)**

         (*b*) $x^2 - x - 12$.   **(2)**

4   The population of gulls in a coastal town is increasing at a constant rate
     of 3% every year. At present there are estimated to be 3000 gulls. What
     will the population of gulls be after 4 years? (Remember to give your
     answer as a whole number of gulls.)   **(3)**

Marks

5 Find the coordinates of the point of intersection of the straight lines
with equations $\begin{cases} 2x + y = 1 \\ x + 3y = 13. \end{cases}$

(4)

6 This rectangle and this square have equal perimeters.
The measurements are in centimetres.

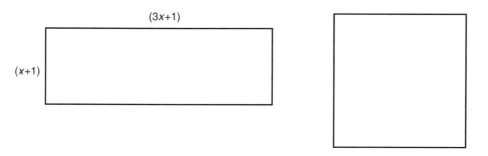

(3x+1)

(x+1)

Calculate the length of a side of the square in terms of *x*.

(2)

7M Write down the period of the graph of $y = 2\cos(3x)°$.

(1)

8A Harry earns £12·68 per hour for a 40-hour week. He is paid for 52 weeks in the year. His tax allowances amount to £4630. Tax is payable on whole pounds only and the current rates of tax are:

for the first £1880 of taxable income	10p in the £
for the next £26,880 of taxable income	22p in the £
for the rest of the taxable income	40p in the £

Calculate Harry's annual earnings, annual tax, and hence his weekly take-home pay.

(9)

Marks

9   The graph of $y = \sin x°$ for $0 \le x \le 360$ is shown below.

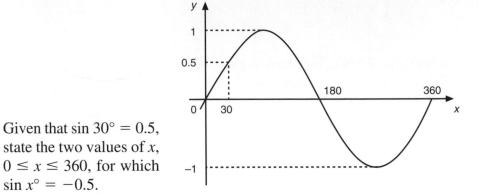

Given that $\sin 30° = 0.5$,
state the two values of x,
$0 \le x \le 360$, for which
$\sin x° = -0.5$.

(2)

10   (*a*)   Calculate the volume of soup in a can
measuring 9·2 cm high with a diameter
of 6·7 cm, expressing your answer in
cubic centimetres correct to 3 significant figures.

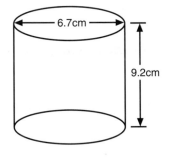

(4)

(*b*)   All of the soup is poured into a cylindrical mug of diameter
7·7 cm. Calculate the depth of soup in the mug, giving your
answer in centimetres correct to two significant figures.

(3)

11M (*a*)   Change the subject of the formula $p = at + u$ to t.

(2)

(*b*)   Solve correct to one decimal place $2x^2 - 5x - 6 = 0$.

(4)

Marks

12 Pumpkin Software have created a logo for their products.

The logo is drawn as follows:
Triangle ABC is equilateral with each side 4 cm.
Semi-circles are drawn on AB and AC as diameters.
The arc BC has centre A and radius 4 cm.

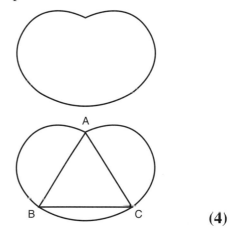

Calculate the perimeter of the logo. **(4)**

13M The cross-section of part of an amateur football cup can be represented by the parabola with equation $y = \frac{1}{4}(x - 1)^2 + 2$.

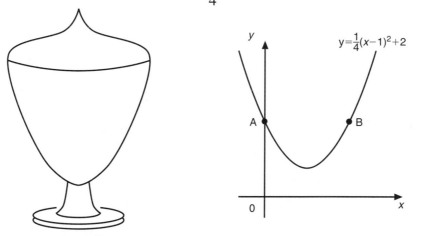

(*a*) Write down the coordinates of the minimum turning point on this parabola. **(2)**

(*b*) Write down the equation of the axis of symmetry. **(1)**

(*c*) The points A and B have the same y-coordinate. Find the coordinates of A and B. **(2)**

Marks

14A The volume of the plumb-bob shown is given
by $V = \dfrac{\pi r^2}{3}(h + 2r)$.

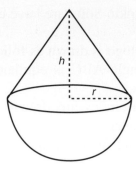

Calculate the value of V when $r = 2$ and $h = 3$, giving your answer correct to 3 significant figures.

(3)

15 To walk from the seventh green (S) to the eighth tee (T), golfers must cross a burn via a bridge at right angles to the burn to a point A, as shown, and then follow a path parallel to the burn.

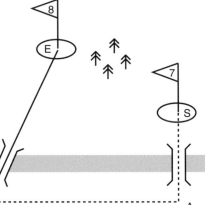

Being held up by slow play ahead, a golfer measured the bearings of S and E from T. He had previously noticed that the distance from S to A was 20 metres.

His caddy knew the distance TE to be 230 metres.

When he got back to the club house he was able to draw this plan.

From his plan he was able to calculate the distance from E to S.

Show the working that he should have produced and find his answer.

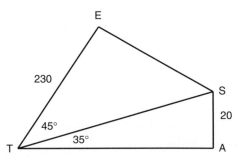

(5)

Marks

16A Calculate the mean height of the runners in an under-15 cross-country race from this frequency table.

height (h cm)	frequency
$62 \cdot 5 < h \leq 63 \cdot 5$	4
$63 \cdot 5 < h \leq 64 \cdot 5$	7
$64 \cdot 5 < h \leq 65 \cdot 5$	13
$65 \cdot 5 < h \leq 66 \cdot 5$	12
$66 \cdot 5 < h \leq 67 \cdot 5$	16
$67 \cdot 5 < h \leq 68 \cdot 5$	11
$68 \cdot 5 < h \leq 69 \cdot 5$	7

(5)

17M (*a*) Solve the equation $5\cos x^\circ - 1 = 0$ for $0 \leq x \leq 360$. **(3)**

(*b*) Show that $\tan^2 A(1 - \sin^2 A) = \sin^2 A$. **(2)**

Total: 71 marks

[END OF QUESTION PAPER]

15

Intermediate 2
Mathematics
Paper 1 – Non-calculator

PRACTICE PAPER B

NATIONAL
QUALIFICATIONS
Time: 45 minutes

You may *NOT* use a calculator.

**Candidates doing units 1, 2 and 3 should omit questions 6A, 9A.
Candidates doing units 1, 2 and Applications of Mathematics should omit
questions 4M, 7M, 8M.**

Marks

1   This stem and leaf diagram shows the trade-in allowances offered by 25 different garages for John's car.

$$
\begin{array}{c|ccccccc}
2 & 0 & 4 & 5 & 9 & & & \\
3 & 0 & 0 & 0 & 2 & 5 & 7 & 9 \\
4 & 0 & 5 & 8 & 8 & 9 & & \\
5 & 0 & 1 & 1 & 3 & 5 & 6 & 7 & 9 \\
6 & 0 & & & & & &
\end{array}
$$

$$ 2 \mid 1 \quad \text{denotes £2100} $$

    (*a*)   For this data, find (i)   the median,   **(1)**

                          (ii) the lower and upper quartiles,   **(2)**

                          (iii) the semi-interquartile range.   **(2)**

    (*b*)   If one of these garages were to be chosen at random, what is the probability that it would offer John more than £5000 for his car?   **(1)**

2   Multiply out the brackets and collect the like terms

$$(x + 2)(3x^2 + 2x - 1).$$ **(3)**

Marks

3   Factorise   (*a*) $16x^2 - 9y^2$.   **(2)**

(*b*) $x^2 + 3x - 28$.   **(2)**

4M   This diagram shows the graph of $y = p \cos x°$.

State the value of *p*.

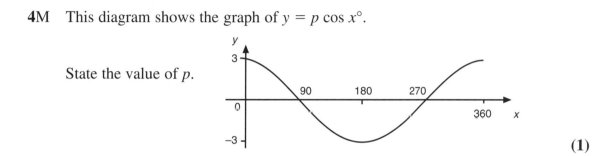

(1)

5   The contents of 20 boxes of drawing pins were counted, giving these results.

| 51 | 49 | 48 | 48 | 44 | 49 | 46 | 52 | 45 | 50 |
| 46 | 47 | 48 | 47 | 50 | 48 | 51 | 47 | 49 | 50 |

(*a*)   Construct a dot plot for this data.   **(2)**

(*b*)   Describe the shape of the distribution.   **(1)**

(*c*)   What would you expect the 'average contents per box' to be?   **(1)**

6A   The area of this trapezium is given by

$$A = \frac{1}{2}(a + b)\,h.$$

(*a*)   Find *A* when $a = 3$, $b = 5$, and $h = 4$.   **(3)**

(*b*)   Find *a* when $A = 25$, $b = 6$, and $h = 5$.   **(3)**

Marks

7M Change the subject of the formula $w = 3t^2 - v$ to t.   **(3)**

8M (*a*) Express $\sqrt{12} - \sqrt{3} + \sqrt{27}$ as a single surd in its simplest form.   **(3)**

(*b*) Express $\dfrac{2}{x} - \dfrac{3}{x + 1}$ as a single fraction in its simplest form.   **(3)**

Marks

9A Sandy is retired and organises his activities according to this flowchart.

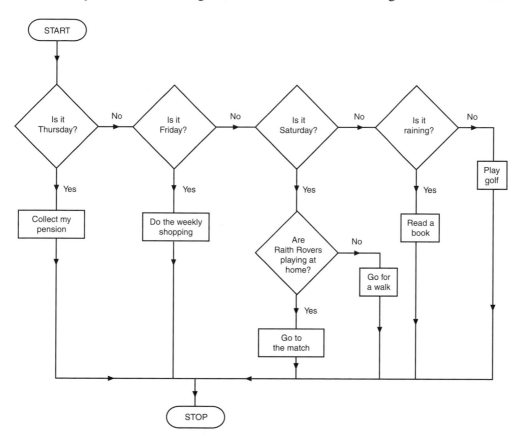

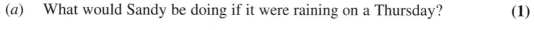

(*a*) What would Sandy be doing if it were raining on a Thursday? **(1)**

(*b*) When does he go for a walk? **(2)**

(*c*) What is the greatest number of days in any week on which you might find Sandy reading a book? **(1)**

Total: 37 marks

[END OF QUESTION PAPER]

PRACTICE PAPER B

Calculators may be used in this paper.

**Candidates doing units 1, 2 and 3 should omit questions 5A, 10A, 14A.
Candidates doing units 1, 2 and Applications of Mathematics should omit
questions 6M, 9M, 11M, 13M.**

Marks

1   A golf club committee consists of six men and six women.

    (*a*)   The ages of the men are   51   56   47   61   45   58.

          Use appropriate formulae to calculate the mean and standard deviation, showing all your working clearly.   **(4)**

    (*b*)   The ages of the women have a mean of 49 and a standard deviation of 6·4. Compare the ages of these men and these women.   **(2)**

2   A milk tanker has a cylindrical tank and the driver can measure the depth of milk in the tank with a rod, as shown.

The radius of the tank (AC) is 1·2 metres. Calculate the width of the surface of the milk (AB) when the depth of the milk is 2 metres.   **(4)**

Marks

3   Robert wishes to invest £2000 for three years. Is it better to choose:

   (*a*)   The Plus Bond which pays 2·5% compound interest per annum, or

   (*b*)   The Premier Bond which pays 8% on maturity?

   (4)

4   The cost of hiring a petrol-driven chain saw depends on the number of days the saw is taken for and the number of litres of petrol used up.

   (*a*)   Bill hired a chain saw for 5 days and used 4 litres of petrol. This cost £128. Let the cost of the hire be £x per day, and the cost of petrol be £y per litre. Write down an equation involving x and y which models Bill's expenditure.

   (1)

   (*b*)   Sarah hired the same saw the following week (at the same rates) for 3 days and used 2 litres of petrol. This cost £76·50.
   Write down a second equation involving x and y to model Sarah's expenditure.

   (1)

   (*c*)   Find what it costs per day to hire this chain saw and the cost of a litre of petrol.

   (4)

5A   The fee for marking a certain exam script is £1·78.
   Each marker is also paid a general fee equivalent to an additional 50 scripts.
   This is all taxed at the basic rate (22%).
   A certain marker attended a markers' meeting and claimed travelling expenses (which are not taxed) for 86 miles at 27·7p per mile.
   Calculate how much the marker receives altogether for marking 287 scripts.

   (6)

Marks

6M

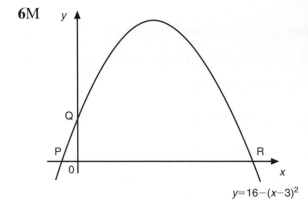

$y = 16 - (x - 3)^2$

The equation of this parabola is $y = 16 - (x - 3)^2$.

(a) Write down the coordinates of the maximum turning point. **(2)**

(b) Find the coordinates of Q. **(2)**

(c) Given that R is the point $(7, 0)$, find the coordinates of P. **(1)**

7 A cylindrical ice-cream cooler has an internal diameter of 45 cm and a height of 40 cm.

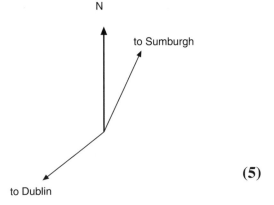

(a) Calculate the maximum volume of ice-cream this cooler can hold. Give your answer in cubic centimetres correct to 2 significant figures. **(4)**

(b) If a scoop of ice-cream is a sphere of radius 2·5 cm, how many scoops of ice-cream can this cooler hold? **(3)**

8 Two planes leave Edinburgh airport at approximately the same time.

One flies on a bearing of 015° towards Sumburgh at a speed of 280 m.p.h.

The other flies on a bearing of 215° towards Dublin at a speed of 340 m.p.h.

To the nearest mile, how far apart are they after half an hour? **(5)**

N

to Sumburgh

to Dublin

Marks

9M   (*a*)   Expand and simplify $a^{\frac{1}{2}}(a^{\frac{2}{3}} + 2a^{-1})$.   **(2)**

       (*b*)   Solve, correct to one decimal place, $3x^2 + 4x - 5 = 0$.   **(4)**

10A   <u>Lofty Loans monthly repayment table</u>

I : including payment protection   E : excluding payment protection

LOAN AMOUNT		£1000	£2000	£3000	£4000
12 months repayment	I	£113·09	£224·96	£337·25	£449·82
	E	£98·89	£195·17	£292·37	£389·74
24 months repayment	I	£58·65	£117·82	£176·83	£232·51
	E	£51·97	£103·23	£155·06	£204·87
36 months repayment	I	£41·32	£87·74	£122·36	£163·53
	E	£36·02	£71·85	£107·85	£143·75

Jennifer wishes to borrow £4000 to improve her kitchen.

(*a*)   Find the total repayment cost if she opts for repayment over 24 months including payment protection.   **(3)**

(*b*)   Calculate how much less she would have to pay if she took the same loan without payment protection.   **(3)**

Marks

11M The graph of $y = \sin x°$ is shown below by the broken line. The solid line has equation $y = \sin(x + k)°$.

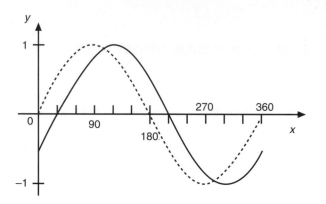

Write down the value of k. **(1)**

12 'The Sharp End' is a new restaurant due to open soon in Sauchiecaddens Avenue. It has a modified arrowhead for a logo.

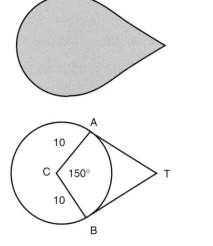

The arrowhead was designed by drawing a circle with centre C and radius 10 cm.
Two radii CA and CB are drawn, 150° apart.
The tangents at A and B meet at T.

Calculate the perimeter of the arrowhead. **(5)**

13M (*a*) Solve the equation $3\sin x° + 2 = 0$ for $0 \le x \le 360$. **(3)**

(*b*) Show that $\cos^2 x \tan^2 x = \sin^2 x$. **(2)**

Marks

14A Calculate the average flying experience for the group of pilots represented by this frequency table.

number of hours	10–14	15–19	20–24	25–29	30–34	35–39	40–44
frequency	3	6	8	10	7	5	4

(5)

Total: 71 marks

[END OF QUESTION PAPER]

Intermediate 2
Mathematics
Paper 1 – Non-calculator

PRACTICE PAPER C

NATIONAL QUALIFICATIONS
Time: 45 minutes

You may *NOT* use a calculator.

**Candidates doing units 1, 2 and 3 should omit questions 5A, 8A.
Candidates doing units 1, 2 and Applications of Mathematics should omit questions 4M, 6M.**

Marks

1   After the first five games of the football season, the numbers of goals scored by the 22 teams in the premier and first divisions were as shown below.

    | 5 | 11 | 2 | 4 | 2 | 1 | 6 | 2 | 3 | 2 | 4 |
    | 0 | 11 | 3 | 2 | 4 | 4 | 3 | 3 | 3 | 0 | 1 |

(*a*)   Construct a frequency table for this data and add a cumulative frequency column.   **(2)**

(*b*)   Find the probability that a team chosen at random from these divisions scored an odd number of goals.   **(1)**

2   (*a*)   Expand the brackets and collect the like terms

$$7k + (4k - 1)(2k + 3).$$ **(3)**

(*b*)   Factorise   (i) $8y^2 - 4y$.   **(1)**

(ii) $x^2 - 100$.   **(1)**

Marks

3 A youth club for boys meets weekly. The 23 boys in the club were asked how many times each had been late for school so far that session. The results are shown below.

3	5	0	6	2	3	1	1	0	4	0	2
4	1	2	1	0	4	2	0	5	2	1	

(*a*) For this data find the median and the quartiles. **(3)**

(*b*) Construct a box plot for this data. **(2)**

The same boys were also asked how often each had been late for the youth club during the same period. The box plot for this data is shown below.

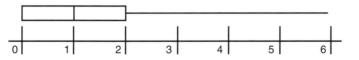

(*c*) (i) Compare the two sets of data. **(1)**

(ii) Discuss the validity of your comparison. **(1)**

Marks

4M This diagram shows the graph of the parabola with equation $y = 4 - (x + 3)^2$.

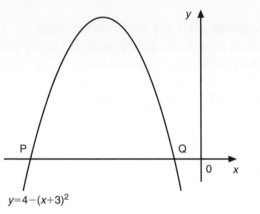

$y=4-(x+3)^2$

(a) State the coordinates of the maximum turning point. **(2)**

(b) State the equation of the axis of symmetry of the parabola. **(1)**

(c) The parabola cuts the x-axis at P and Q. Find the length of PQ. **(3)**

5A The diagram shows two masses m and n connected by a cord passing over a smooth pulley. The acceleration of this connected system is given by

$$a = \left(\frac{m - n}{m + n}\right)g.$$

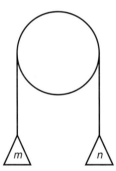

(a) Calculate a when $m = 5$, $n = 3$ and $g = 32$. **(3)**

(b) Calculate g when $a = 4$, $m = 9$ and $n = 7$. **(3)**

6M (a) Express $5\sqrt{7} - \sqrt{28}$ as a single surd in its simplest form. **(2)**

(b) Express $\dfrac{1}{x} - \dfrac{1}{x^2}$ as a single fraction in its simplest form. **(2)**

Marks

7 Factorise $6x^2 - 13x + 6$. **(2)**

8A This flowchart is used by Alex's Autos to calculate the net cost of a new car listed at a price of £11,500.

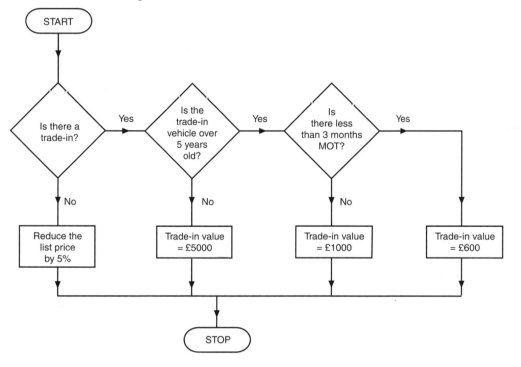

(a) How much would one of these new cars cost against a 7-year old trade-in with one month's MOT? **(2)**

(b) Would it be cheaper to scrap the trade-in vehicle and obtain the no trade-in discount? **(2)**

Total: 37 marks

[END OF QUESTION PAPER]

Intermediate 2
Mathematics
Paper 2

PRACTICE PAPER C

NATIONAL
QUALIFICATIONS
Time: 1 hour 30 minutes

Calculators may be used in this paper.

Candidates doing units 1, 2 and 3 should omit questions 9A, 12A, 16A.
Candidates doing units 1, 2 and Applications of Mathematics should omit
questions 8M, 11M, 14M, 15M.

Marks

1   (*a*)   The number of plums in each of six half-kilogram packs from Sainfield's is shown below.

   13   12   9   11   13   14

Calculate the mean and standard deviation of these numbers, showing clearly the formulae you use and all your working.   **(4)**

   (*b*)   John picked plums from the tree in his garden and weighed out six half-kilogram bags to give to friends. He counted the number of plums in each bag and calculated that his data had a mean of 15 and a standard deviation of 1·79.
Compare the sizes of the plums from John's tree and those from Sainfield's.   **(2)**

2   Calculate the gradient of the line AB

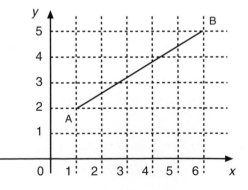

(2)

Marks

3 The diagram on the left represents a bowl, which is in the shape of part of a sphere. AB is a diameter of the circular rim of the bowl.

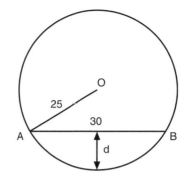

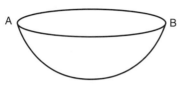

The diagram on the right shows a cross-section, through O, the centre of the sphere of which the bowl is part. AB is 30 cm.
The radius of the sphere is 25 cm.
Calculate the depth, d cm, of the bowl.

(4)

4 A young man has a salary of £24,000 this year, rising by 3% per annum. His father is self-employed and earns £35,000 this year, but he is winding-down and expects a drop in salary of 7% per annum.
How many years will it be before the son earns more per annum than his father?

(5)

5 Use algebra to solve the simultaneous equations $\begin{cases} 2x + 3y = 1 \\ 3x - 2y = 21 \end{cases}$.

(3)

6 During one World Cup competition, chocolate footballs were on sale.
They were spherical and filled with cream, just like Easter eggs.
They had an outer diameter of 45 mm and the chocolate shell was 2 mm thick.

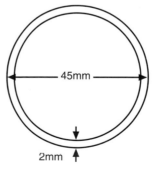

Calculate the volume of chocolate in one football, giving your answer in mm^3 correct to 3 significant figures.

(5)

Marks

7   A man-o'-war sailed 6 miles due North from point A to point B, passing a cliff top C, where a cannon was sited.

At A, the bearing of C was 055°.
At B, the bearing of C was 120°.
The range of the cannon was 4 miles.

Did the man-o'-war come within range of the cannon? (Explain your answer)

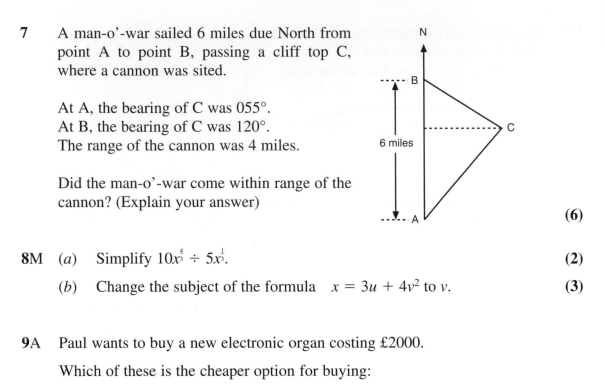

(6)

8M (a) Simplify $10x^{\frac{4}{3}} \div 5x^{\frac{1}{3}}$.   **(2)**

(b) Change the subject of the formula $x = 3u + 4v^2$ to v.   **(3)**

9A Paul wants to buy a new electronic organ costing £2000.

Which of these is the cheaper option for buying:

(a) hire purchase of £500 deposit and 24 monthly instalments of £81·60, or

(b) a bank loan to be repaid at the rate of £97·50 per month for two years?   **(5)**

10 A boat sail has two edges of length 3 m and 6 m and the angle between these edges is 40°, as shown.

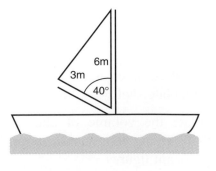

Calculate the area of this sail.   **(2)**

Marks

11M Determine the equation of this parabola.

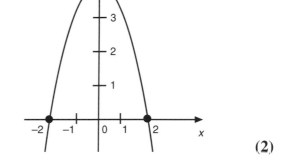

(2)

12A Dick is a salesman with a basic salary of £18,500 plus commission of 8% on sales over £10,000.

(*a*) Calculate his annual income for a year in which he makes sales worth £23,000.

(2)

The rates of tax for that year were:

for the first £1880 of taxable income	10%
for the next £26,880 of taxable income	22%
for the rest of the taxable income	40%

(*b*) Dick's tax allowances amounted to £5000. Calculate his tax bill for that year.

(5)

33

Marks

13 Two spots of rust on the rim of a cycle wheel at points A and B are 35 cm apart, measured along the rim.

The radius of the wheel is 29 cm.

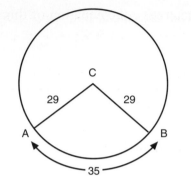

If C is the centre of the wheel, calculate the size of angle ACB.　　　　　　　　　　　　　　**(4)**

14M Solve the equation $4y^2 + 5y - 1 = 0$ correct to two decimal places.　　　　**(4)**

15M The length, L cm, of the space at the top of a cylinder t milliseconds after the piston rod is vertical and going down is given by

$L = 5 + 4 \sin t°, \quad 0 \le t \le 360.$

(*a*)　Find the length of the space after 100 milliseconds.　　　　**(2)**

(*b*)　Find the times when the space is 7 cm long.　　　　**(4)**

Marks

16A The Intermediate 2 marks for the pupils in Dunaber Academy are shown in this frequency table.

mark	41–45	46–50	51–55	56–60	61–65	66–70	71–75	76–80
frequency	8	9	13	16	16	13	11	4

Calculate the mean mark.

(5)

Total: 71 marks

[END OF QUESTION PAPER]

Intermediate 2 Mathematics

PRACTICE PAPER D

NATIONAL QUALIFICATIONS
Time: 45 minutes

Paper 1 – Non-calculator

You may *NOT* use a calculator.

**Candidates doing units 1, 2 and 3 should omit questions 7A, 9A, 11A.
Candidates doing units 1, 2 and Applications of Mathematics should omit questions 5M, 8M, 10M.**

Marks

1 This frequency table shows the ages of the boys in a youth group.

age	f
11	7
12	8
13	6
14	5
15	3

   (*a*) Copy this frequency table and add a cumulative frequency column. **(1)**

   (*b*) Find the median. **(1)**

2   (*a*) Expand $p(2p + 3q)$. **(2)**

   (*b*) Factorise $2a + ax + ay$. **(1)**

Marks

3 TAN is the tangent to the circle at A.
AB is a diameter.

$A\hat{B}C = 60°$.

Calculate the size of angle CAT, showing
all your working.

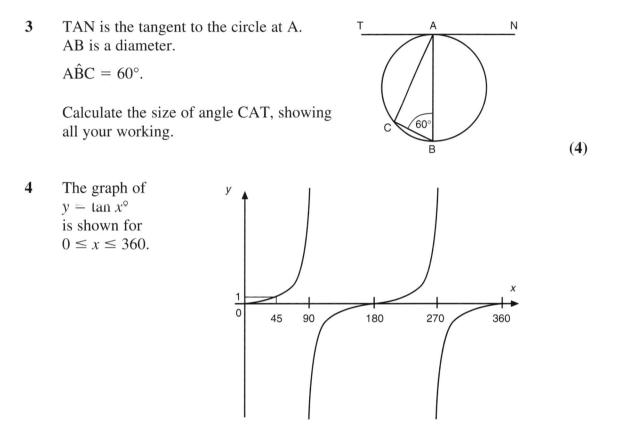

(4)

4 The graph of
$y = \tan x°$
is shown for
$0 \le x \le 360$.

Given that $\tan 45° = 1$, find the two values of x in this interval for which
$\tan x° = -1$.

(2)

5M Solve the equation $2x^2 + 5x - 3 = 0$ by factorising.

(3)

Marks

6 The telephone company Telechat charge their customers a quarterly line rental as well as the cost of their calls at a given rate per unit.

    (*a*) Last quarter, David used 1000 phone units and was charged £30. Let £q be the quarterly line rental and £p be the cost per phone unit. Construct an equation in p and q to model David's situation. **(1)**

    (*b*) In the same quarter, Claire used 1600 phone units and was charged £39. Construct a second equation in p and q to model Claire's situation. **(1)**

    (*c*) Calculate the quarterly line rental and the charge per phone unit. **(4)**

7A The response times of ambulance crews were recorded for the first 60 calls of the week and the results are shown by this cumulative frequency curve.

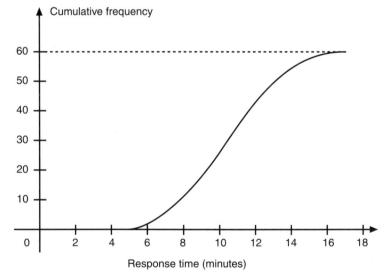

    (*a*) How many calls were responded to within 10 minutes? **(1)**

    (*b*) The target set was to respond to at least 80% of calls within 15 minutes. Was this target achieved? Explain how you arrive at your answer. **(2)**

Marks

8M Copy this sketch of the graph of $y = \sin x°$ for $0 \le x \le 360$.

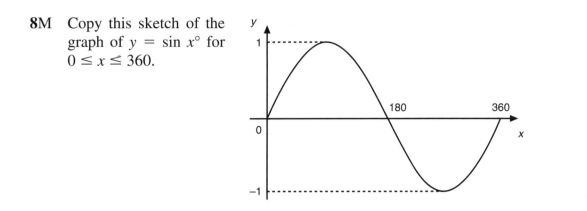

On the same sketch, draw the graph of $y = 3 \sin 2x°$. **(2)**

9A The surface area of this pencil body shape is given by

$$A = 3a\left(2l + \frac{d}{2}\right).$$

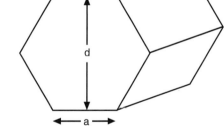

Find d when $A = 665$, $a = 5$, and $l = 20$. **(3)**

10M (*a*) Simplify $\sqrt{20} + \sqrt{5} - \sqrt{45}$. **(3)**

(*b*) Evaluate $5x^{-2}$ when $x = 3$. **(2)**

Marks

11A This flowchart is used to calculate the cost of having raffle tickets printed by Dupliprint.

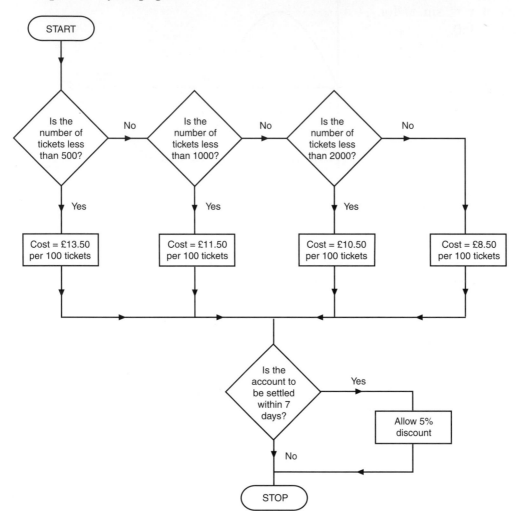

Calculate the cost of having 1500 raffle tickets printed if the bill is to be paid within 7 days.

(4)

Total: 37 marks

[END OF QUESTION PAPER]

Intermediate 2
Mathematics
Paper 2

PRACTICE PAPER D

NATIONAL
QUALIFICATIONS
Time: 1 hour 30 minutes

Calculators may be used in this paper.

**Candidates doing units 1, 2 and 3 should omit questions 8A, 12A, 15A.
Candidates doing units 1, 2 and Applications of Mathematics should omit
questions 6M, 9M, 11M, 14M, 17M.**

Marks

1   Factorise $25 - 4k^2$.   **(2)**

2   AB is a chord of a circle with centre C and radius 13 cm.
AB = 24 cm.
M is the mid-point of AB.

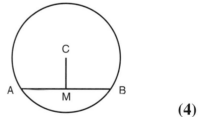

Calculate the length of CM.   **(4)**

3   A coin is tossed and a die (a dice) is rolled.

(*a*)   List all the possible outcomes.   **(1)**

(*b*)   Which is more likely: (i)   a head and an even number,

                        or   (ii)   a tail and a factor of 6?

Explain your answer.   **(2)**

Marks

4 A man invests £200 for 3 years in a bank paying 3% compound interest per annum. Calculate the total interest his money earns in this period. **(4)**

5 A plumb-bob is in the shape of a cone sur-mounted on a hemisphere.

The diameter of the hemisphere is 6 cm. The slant height of the cone is 5 cm.

Calculate the volume of the plumb-bob in cm³, expressing your answer correct to 2 significant figures.

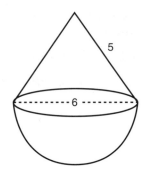

(5)

6M Change the subject of the formula $A = \left(\dfrac{a+b}{2}\right)h$ to a, expressing a as a single fraction. **(4)**

7 A regular octagon PQRSTUVW is drawn inside a circle with centre C and radius 8 cm.

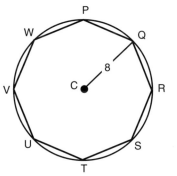

Calculate the area of the octagon PQRSTUVW. **(5)**

Marks

8A Bob is a builder. His basic rate of pay is £9.50 per hour for an 8-hour day.
- He is paid overtime at time-and-a-half if he works more than 8 hours in a day.
- He is paid overtime at time-and-a-half if he works on a Saturday forenoon.
- He is paid overtime at double-time if he works on a Saturday afternoon.

Here is his time sheet for last week.

	Start	Finish	Start	Finish
Monday	08:00	12:30	13:00	16:30
Tuesday	08:00	12:30	13:00	16:30
Wednesday	08:00	12:30	13:00	17:30
Thursday	08:00	12:30	13:00	17:30
Friday	08:00	12:30	13:00	16:30
Saturday	08:00	14:00		

Calculate his gross pay for the week. **(5)**

9M This diagram shows the graph of
$y = kx^2 + 1$.

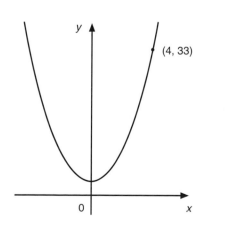

(4, 33)

Find the value of k. **(2)**

Marks

10 This diagram represents a shot-putt circle and the sector into which the shot must land to constitute a valid putt.

The diameter of the shot-putt circle (the smaller one) is 2·135 metres.

The length of AC and BC is 80 m, and $\hat{ACB} = 45°$.

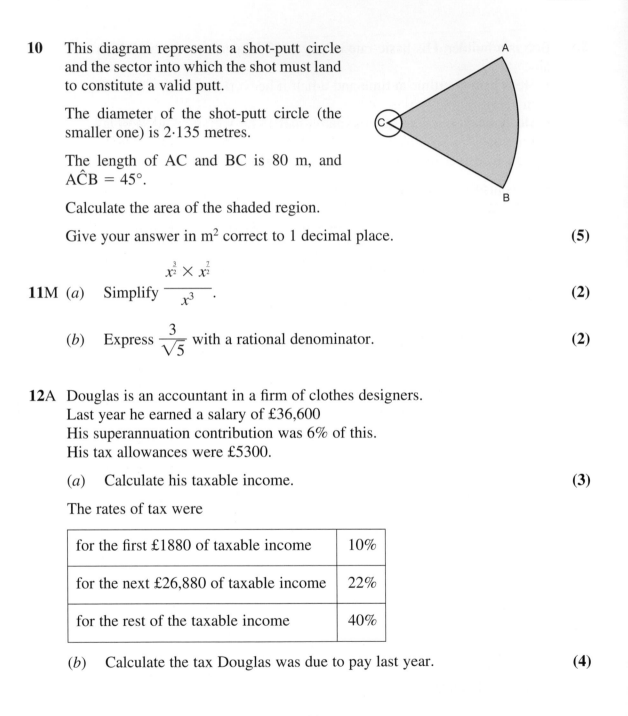

Calculate the area of the shaded region.

Give your answer in m² correct to 1 decimal place. **(5)**

11M (*a*) Simplify $\dfrac{x^{\frac{3}{2}} \times x^{\frac{7}{2}}}{x^3}$. **(2)**

(*b*) Express $\dfrac{3}{\sqrt{5}}$ with a rational denominator. **(2)**

12A Douglas is an accountant in a firm of clothes designers.
Last year he earned a salary of £36,600
His superannuation contribution was 6% of this.
His tax allowances were £5300.

(*a*) Calculate his taxable income. **(3)**

The rates of tax were

for the first £1880 of taxable income	10%
for the next £26,880 of taxable income	22%
for the rest of the taxable income	40%

(*b*) Calculate the tax Douglas was due to pay last year. **(4)**

Marks

13 A physics class of 20 pupils spent 4 weeks studying the topic 'Sound'.
During this time they were given 12 pieces of homework.
At the end they were given a 30-minute test out of 20 marks. One pupil
was absent and missed the test.
This scatter-graph illustrates the connection between the mark attained
in the test and the number of pieces of homework which were not done.

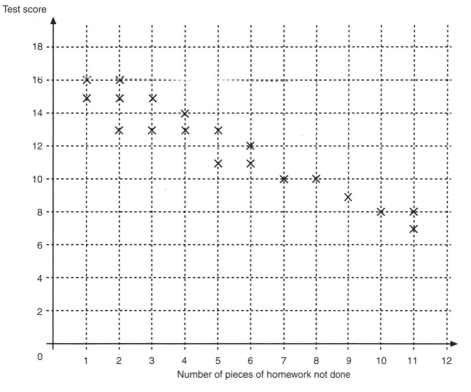

Number of pieces of homework not done

(*a*) Draw (on the question paper) the best fitting straight line and
determine its equation, showing all your working. **(3)**

(*b*) Sandy missed the test and failed to do his homework on 4 occa-
sions. **Use your equation** of the regression line to estimate
Sandy's score in this 'Sound' test. **(2)**

(*c*) How confident would you be (and why) about awarding Sandy
this estimate? **(1)**

Marks

14M Solve the equation $3 \cos x° - 1 = 0$ for $0 \leq x \leq 360$. **(3)**

15A All of the Intermediate 2 pupils in one school counted up the number of aunts uncles and cousins each had, and collated their information in this frequency table.

no. of relatives	0	1–5	6–10	11–15	16–20	21–25	26–30	31–35	36–40
frequency	0	8	13	15	17	12	8	5	3

Calculate the mean number of aunts uncles and cousins in this group. **(5)**

16 A joiner is making a children's chute.
The slide is to be at 40° to the horizontal.
The stairs are to be at 65° to the horizontal.
The slide is to be 2 metres long.

Calculate the length of wood needed for the stairs. **(3)**

17M (*a*) Simplify $\dfrac{x^2 + x}{x^3}$. **(2)**

(*b*) Hence express $\dfrac{x^2 + x}{x^3} + \dfrac{1}{x}$ as a single fraction in its simplest form. **(2)**

Total: 71 marks

[END OF QUESTION PAPER]

Intermediate 2
Mathematics

Paper 1 – Non-calculator

NATIONAL QUALIFICATIONS
Time: 45 minutes

You may *NOT* use a calculator.

**Candidates doing units 1, 2 and 3 should omit questions 8A, 10A.
Candidates doing units 1, 2 and Applications of Mathematics should omit questions 7M, 9M.**

Marks

1   (*a*)   Find the median and the semi-interquartile range for the data in this stem and leaf diagram.

3	0	0	5		
3	6	6	6	7	
4	1	1	1	1	3 5
4	7	7	7	8	
5	0	1	2	2	
5	3	3	3		

5 | 7   denotes 57   **(5)**

       (*b*)   Convert the data in this stem and leaf diagram into the form of a frequency table and add a cumulative frequency column.   **(2)**

Marks

2   Find the equation of the straight line shown.

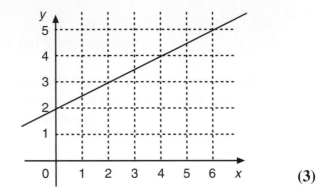

(3)

3   Factorise $36x^2 - 49y^2$.

(2)

4   Given that cos 800° = 0·174, write down the value of cos 80°.

(1)

5   Factorise $x^2 - 2x - 3$.

(2)

6   Find the coordinates of the point of intersection of the lines with equations

$$\begin{cases} x = 2 \\ 3x + 4y = 18. \end{cases}$$

(2)

7M   (*a*)   Simplify $\dfrac{(2x + 3)^4}{(2x + 3)^2}$.

(1)

(*b*)   Express $\dfrac{2}{x} + \dfrac{3}{y}$ as a single fraction.

(2)

(*c*)   Change the subject of the formula $m = kt + r$ to *t*.

(2)

Marks

8A This diagram shows the mouth of a railway tunnel.
The stone work forms part of a rectangle and the tunnel is in the shapc of a parabola.

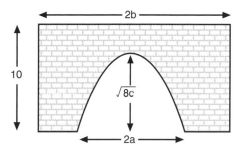

The area of stonework is given by

$$A = 20b - 16a + \frac{2}{3}\left(\frac{a^3}{c}\right).$$

(*a*) Calculate A when $a = 4$, $b = 5$ and $c = 2$. **(3)**

(*b*) Calculate c when $A = 33\frac{1}{3}$, $a = 2$ and $b = 3$. **(3)**

9M (*a*) Simplify $(2x^{\frac{2}{3}})^2$. **(2)**

(*b*) Express $\dfrac{3}{2 + \sqrt{5}}$ with a rational denominator. **(3)**

10A This flowchart can be used to find the cost of a theatre ticket.

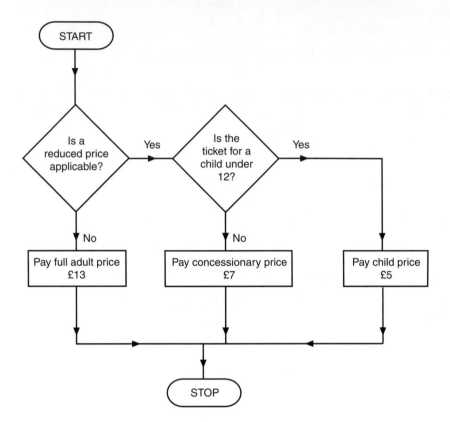

Use the flowchart to find the total cost of 7 tickets:
2 adults, 4 concessions, and 1 child under 12. **(4)**

Total: 37 marks

[END OF QUESTION PAPER]

Intermediate 2
Mathematics
Paper 2

PRACTICE PAPER E

NATIONAL
QUALIFICATIONS
Time: 1 hour 30 minutes

Calculators may be used in this paper.

**Candidates doing units 1, 2 and 3 should omit questions 9A, 12A, 14A.
Candidates doing units 1, 2 and Applications of Mathematics should omit
questions 8M, 13M.**

Marks

1   (*a*)   The numbers of matches in six boxes were as shown below.

53   47   51   49   52   54

Showing all your working, calculate the standard deviation.   **(4)**

(*b*)   If one of these boxes of matches were chosen at random, find the
probability of it containing an even number of matches.   **(2)**

2   Find the equation of the straight line shown in this diagram.

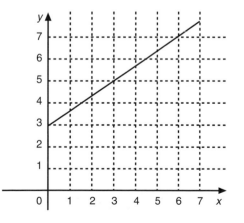

(3)

Marks

3 TP is the tangent at T to the circle with centre C.
The line CP meets the circle at R.
CR = 8 cm and RP = 9 cm.

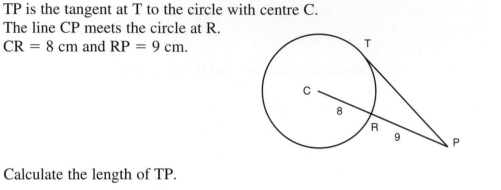

Calculate the length of TP. **(4)**

4 (*a*) Factorise completely $3k^2 - 9k$. **(1)**

(*b*) Expand the brackets and collect the like terms

$$(x - 2)(x^2 - 3x + 4).$$ **(3)**

5 Peter and Paul started work at the same time.
Peter was given an annual salary of £15,000 with an annual increase of 4%.
Paul was given an annual salary of £16,000 with an annual increase of 2%.
After how many years did Peter's salary exceed Paul's?
[Show all your working.] **(5)**

Marks

6 A triangular field lies between two roads as shown.
The edges of the field along the road sides are 40 m and 70 m in length.
The roads meet at an angle of 63°.

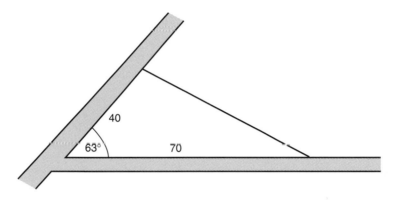

Calculate the area of the field. **(2)**

Marks

7 A church magazine is produced on A4 paper folded in half to make A5 pages. Thus the number of pages in each magazine is a multiple of 4. Three printing firms have submitted their prices to produce sufficient magazines for the whole congregation. Their rates are:

- Fastprint £8 per page.
- Quickprint £20 + £7 per page.
- Rapidprint £40 + £5 per page.

The graph of cost against number of pages for each firm is shown below.

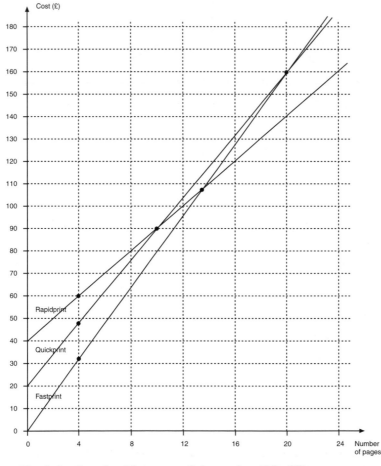

(*a*) Explain the significance of the point (10, 90). **(2)**

(*b*) What advice would you give to the magazine editor to secure the lowest cost? **(2)**

54

Marks

8M The graph of $y = (x - 3)^2 - 1$ is shown.

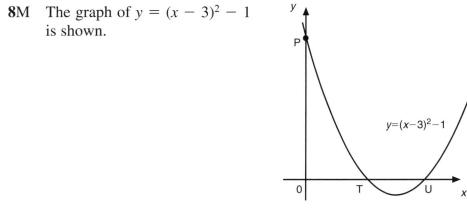

(a) State the coordinates of the minimum turning point. **(2)**

(b) Given that P and Q have the same y-coordinate, find the coordinates of Q. **(3)**

(c) Find the coordinates of T and U. **(3)**

9A Tom's pay slip for last month is partially completed and is shown below. Tom is paid a basic monthly salary of £1500 plus 11% commission on his monthly sales.

Basic	Commission	Bonus	Gross Salary
£1500		£200	
National Insurance	Income Tax	Superannuation	Total Deductions
£163	£312·64		
		Net Salary	

(a) Calculate Tom's gross salary for last month when his sales totalled £5500. **(2)**

(b) From Tom's gross salary, 8% is deducted for his superannuation fund. Calculate his net salary for last month. **(3)**

Marks

10 Dublin is famous for its Georgian front doors. The fanlight above one such door consists of a semi-circle with 5 sectors, as shown. The central piece is slightly larger than the others.

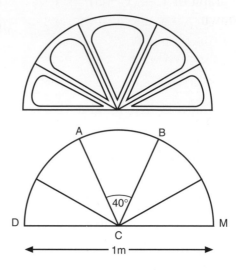

If the diameter DM is 1 metre and AĈB = 40°, calculate the length of the arc AB. Express your answer in centimetres correct to the nearest millimetre.

(4)

11

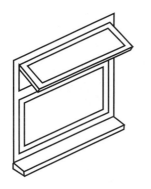

The diagram on the left represents an open hopper window. The hopper has been swung open through 35°.

The diagram on the right shows the end view.

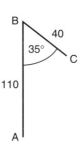

The height of the complete window AB is 110 cm.
The depth of the hopper window BC is 40 cm.

The hinges have become slack and the hopper needs to be propped open with a stick. Calculate the length of the stick needed to fit between A and C.

(5)

Marks

12A These are the monthly repayments for a bank loan as advertised via a mail drop.
The upper row of figures for each loan includes payment protection.
The lower row gives the repayment without protection.

APR	Loan	1 year	2 years	3 years	4 years	5 years
8·4%	£15,000	£1425·82 £1306·19	£765·76 £679·46	£548·58 £471·01	£377·64 £305·09	£309·78 £234·75
9·5%	£10,000	£955·65 £875·47	£515·67 £457·56	£371·12 £318·64	£257·72 £208·21	£213·14 £161·52
9·7%	£5000	£478·32 £438·19	£258·34 £229·23	£186·09 £159·77	£129·44 £104·58	£107·22 £81·25
12·8%	£3000	£291·32 £266·88	£159·42 £141·45	£116·29 £99·84	£82·84 £66·92	£70·13 £53·15
15·5%	£2000	£196·69 £180·18	£108·81 £96·55	£80·20 £68·86	£58·24 £47·06	£50·18 £38·02
16·4%	£1000	£98·75 £90·47	£54·83 £48·65	£40·55 £34·92	£29·63 £23·94	£25·67 £19·45

Mr and Mrs Smith each wish to borrow £5000 over 3 years (with protection) to put towards changing their cars.

(*a*) Calculate the total repayment cost for Mr Smith. **(3)**

(*b*) How much would they save if Mr Smith borrowed £10,000 in a single loan? **(3)**

(*c*) Why is the second option cheaper? **(1)**

Marks

13M (*a*) Solve $3x^2 + x - 2 = 0$ by factorising. **(3)**

(*b*) Express $\sqrt{72} - \sqrt{2} + \sqrt{32}$ as a single surd in its simplest form. **(3)**

(*c*) Solve the equation $3 \cos x° - 2 = 0$ for $0 \leq x \leq 360$. **(3)**

14A A fire brigade recorded the number of calls out per day that they received over a three month period. Their results are shown in this frequency table.

calls out per day	frequency
0–1	31
2–3	39
4–5	17
6–7	2
8–9	1

Calculate the mean number of calls out per day. **(5)**

Total: 71 marks

[END OF QUESTION PAPER]

Intermediate 2
Mathematics
Paper 1 – Non-calculator

PRACTICE PAPER F

NATIONAL
QUALIFICATIONS
Time: 45 minutes

You may *NOT* use a calculator.

Candidates doing units 1, 2 and 3 should omit questions 6A, 9A.
Candidates doing units 1, 2 and Applications of Mathematics should omit questions 5M, 8M, 10M.

Marks

1 (a) Expand $(x - 1)(x^2 + 4)$.   **(2)**

   (b) Factorise $25p^2 - 9q^2$.   **(2)**

2 Make a rough sketch of the straight line with equation $y = 8 - 2x$.   **(3)**

3 (a) Given that $\cos 40° = 0{\cdot}766$, write down the value of $\cos 400°$.   **(1)**

   (b) Given that $\cos 75° = 0{\cdot}259$, find the value of q ($180 < q < 360$)
      for which $\cos q° = -0{\cdot}259$.   **(1)**

4 A card is drawn from a standard pack of 52 cards.

   (a) What is the probability of obtaining a black queen?   **(1)**

   (b) If a black queen is drawn and not replaced in the pack, and then a
      second card is drawn, what is the probability of obtaining a
      diamond?   **(2)**

Marks

5M Copy this sketch of the graph of $y = \cos x°$ for $0 \leqslant x \leqslant 360$.

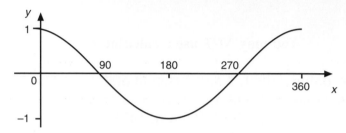

On your copy, sketch the graph of $y = \cos (x - 90)°$. **(2)**

6A Hamish wants to go abroad with the Tartan Army to support Scotland. The travel package costs £590.

He works in Asways for 4 hours each Thursday and Friday, and for 6 hours each Saturday.

His basic rate of pay is £4·20 per hour. He is paid time-and-a-half on Saturdays.

If he saves his earnings for 8 weeks, will this cover the cost of the travel package? **(4)**

Marks

7   Some pupils sat Maths and Physics tests.
Their scores are illustrated by this scatter-graph.

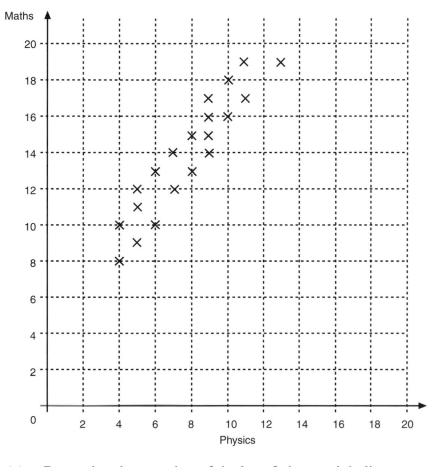

(*a*)   Determine the equation of the best fitting straight line.   **(3)**

(*b*)   Hence estimate the Maths mark for a pupil who was absent for the
Maths test but who scored 12 in the Physics test.   **(2)**

Marks

8M (*a*) (i) Simplify $\sqrt{27}$.

(ii) Hence express $\dfrac{2}{\sqrt{27}}$ with a rational denominator. **(3)**

(*b*) Simplify $p^{\frac{3}{4}} \times 2p^{\frac{5}{4}}$. **(2)**

9A The area, A square centimetres, of the triangle shown

p cm

h cm

q cm

is given by $A = \dfrac{1}{2}(p + q)h$. **(3)**

(*a*) Calculate A when $p = 4$, $q = 5$ and $h = 7$. **(3)**

(*b*) Calculate h when $A = 66$, $p = 3$ and $q = 9$.

(3)

10M Solve the equation $x^2 - 8x + 15 = 0$ by factorising.

Total: 37 marks

[END OF QUESTION PAPER]

Intermediate 2
Mathematics
Paper 2

PRACTICE PAPER F

NATIONAL
QUALIFICATIONS
Time: 1 hour 30 minutes

Calculators may be used in this paper.

**Candidates doing units 1, 2 and 3 should omit questions 9A, 16A, 17A.
Candidates doing units 1, 2 and Applications of Mathematics should omit
questions 7M, 12M, 13M, 14M, 15M.**

Marks

1 An inspector measured the volume of eleven glasses of wine served by
the Royal Hotel, and recorded the results in millilitres as shown below.

   125   127   124   126   127   125   129   123   126   127   123

(*a*) For the above data, find the median and the lower and upper
   quartiles. **(2)**

(*b*) Does this hotel give a fair measure for a 125 ml glass of wine? **(1)**

(*c*) Construct a box plot for this data. **(2)**

(*d*) The inspector carried out similar measurements for the Queen's
   Hotel across the road and drew the following box plot for this
   data.

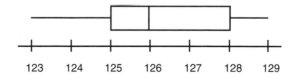

   In which hotel would one rather buy a glass of wine?
   (Give a reason for your answer.) **(1)**

Marks

2   AB is a diameter of the circle with centre C
     and passing through D.

     The length of CD is 5 cm.
     The length of BD is 6 cm.

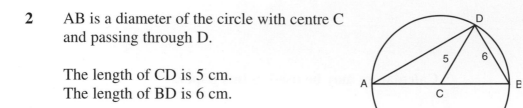

     Calculate the length of AD.   **(4)**

3   Christine's monthly paper bill has just risen by 20% to £39. What was
     it before this increase?   **(3)**

4   Find the equation of the straight line passing through the point $(0, 9)$ and
     parallel to the line with equation $2x - y = 7$.   **(3)**

5   The cost of hiring a car from Mavis Self Drive depends on the number
     of days for which the car is hired and the mileage covered.

     (*a*)   Mary hired a Rover 25 for 7 days and covered 500 miles. This
             cost her £225. Suppose the car cost £x per day to hire plus £y per
             100 miles.
             Write down an equation in x and y to reflect Mary's car hire.   **(1)**

     (*b*)   Norman also hired a Rover 25 for 5 days and covered 400 miles,
             which cost him £165.
             Write down a second equation in x and y to reflect Norman's car
             hire.   **(1)**

     (*c*)   Find the cost per day of hiring the car and the cost per 100 miles.   **(4)**

Marks

6   A 'sleeping policeman' in a hospital driveway is 3 metres wide.
Its cross-section is in the shape of a square and two quarter circles.
The edge of the square is 10 cm in length.
The whole structure is made of hard rubber.

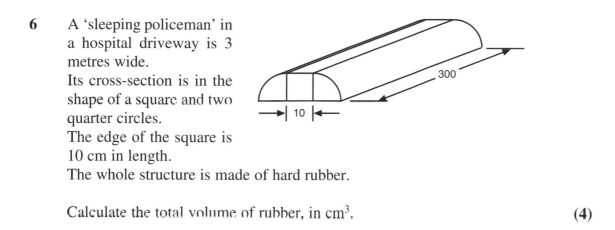

Calculate the total volume of rubber, in cm^3.   **(4)**

7M   This diagram shows the graph of $y = x^2 - 4x + 5$.

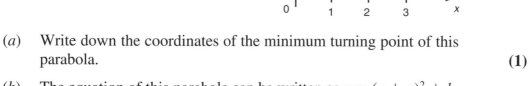

(*a*)   Write down the coordinates of the minimum turning point of this parabola.   **(1)**

(*b*)   The equation of this parabola can be written as $y = (x + a)^2 + b$. Write down the values of *a* and *b*.   **(2)**

Marks

8 A flag pole BC is built into a wall AB and supported by a wire AC as shown.

The flag pole is 2 metres long.
The wire is 3 metres long.

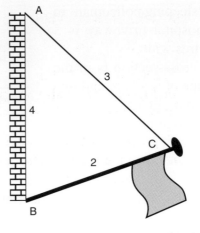

Given that A is 4 metres directly above B, calculate the size of BÂC, correct to 1 decimal place.

(5)

9A Brenda sells jewellery. She earns a basic salary of £8500 plus commission of 10% on all her sales.

(*a*) Calculate her earnings for last year when she sold £20,000 worth of jewellery.

(2)

The rates of tax for last year were

for the first £1880 of taxable income	10p in the £
for the next £26,880 of taxable income	22p in the £
for the rest of the taxable income	40p in the £

(*b*) Brenda's tax allowances amounted to £4195.
Calculate her tax bill for the year.

(5)

Marks

10 $V = IR$ is the equation known as Ohm's Law.

(*a*)   Calculate V when $I = 2 \cdot 14$ and $R = 17 \cdot 26$. **(1)**

(*b*)   When asked to do this calculation, a pupil first rounded the value of I to one decimal place and the value of R to 3 significant figures. What value did the pupil obtain? **(2)**

(*c*)   Express the difference in these two answers as a percentage of the original answer (the one in part (a)), giving your answer correct to 2 significant figures. **(1)**

11   Factorise $2x^2 - 3x - 2$. **(2)**

12M Change the subject of the formula $p = \dfrac{4r}{q}$ to r. **(2)**

13M Solve the equation $4 \tan x° + 3 = 0$ for $0 \le x \le 360$. **(3)**

14M (*a*)   Simplify (i) $\dfrac{x}{x^2}$ (ii) $\dfrac{3x + 3}{x^2 - x - 2}$. **(3)**

(*b*)   Hence express $\dfrac{x}{x^2} + \dfrac{3x + 3}{x^2 - x - 2}$ as a single fraction in its simplest form. **(3)**

15M Write down the periods of the graphs with equations

(*a*) $y = \sin 2x°$

(*b*) $y = \cos \dfrac{1}{3}x°$

(*c*) $y = \tan 4x°$. **(3)**

16A This flowchart can be used to find the selling price of a Vauxhall Corsa listed at £9000.

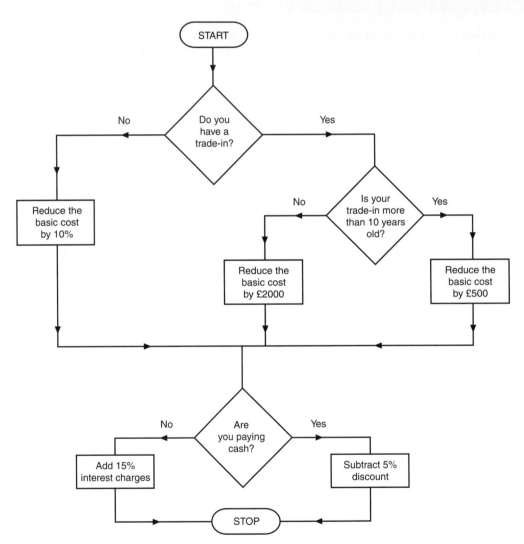

Use the flowchart to calculate the total cost to someone paying cash and trading-in a 1990 Ford Escort.

(5)

Marks

17A A survey was carried out to investigate how long it took in a lawyers' office to answer the telephone.

The results are shown in this frequency table.

time (seconds)	number of calls
20–34	8
35–49	11
50–64	13
65–79	20
80–94	23
95–109	34
110–124	22
125–139	19

Calculate the mean length of time taken to answer the telephone. **(5)**

Total: 71 marks

[END OF QUESTION PAPER]

ANSWERS

PRACTICE PAPER A

Paper 1

1   (*a*)   2   (*b*) $y = 6 - 3x$ **2**   (*a*)

x	f	cum f
5	2	2
6	1	3
7	3	6
8	2	8
9	2	10

(*b*) $\dfrac{2}{5}$

3   75°

4 $k = 4$

5   14 weeks

6   (*a*) $Q_2 = 55$, $Q_1 = 50$, $Q_3 = 57$

     (*b*)   Yes, because the median is over 50 (in fact $\frac{3}{4}$ of all packets are).

     (*c*)

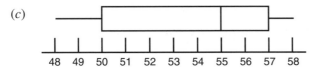

     (*d*)   No, because the median is under 50 (in fact $\frac{3}{4}$ of all packets are).

7 $k = 2$ **8**   (*a*) x^3 (*b*) $\dfrac{5\sqrt{7}}{7}$ (*c*) $\dfrac{7x + 8}{x(x + 2)}$

9   £239·20

PRACTICE PAPER A

Paper 2

1   7·33   **2** $x^3 + x^2 - 5x + 3$ **3**   (*a*) $p(p - 3)$ (*b*) $(x - 4)(x + 3)$

4   3376 or 3377   **5** $(-2, 5)$ **6** $2x + 1$ **7**   120°

8   £26,374·40, £4558, £419·55   **9**   210, 330

10   (*a*)   324 cm³   (*b*)   7·0 cm   **11**   (*a*) $t = \dfrac{p - u}{a}$ (*b*) $-0·9$, 3·4

12   16·8 cm   **13**   (*a*) $(1, 2)$ (*b*) $x = 1$ (*c*)   A $(0, 2\frac{1}{4})$ B$(2, 2\frac{1}{4})$

14   29·3   **15**   207 m   **16**   66·3 cm

17   (*a*)   78·5, 281·5   (*b*)   proof [Use $\cos^2 A = 1 - \sin^2 A$ and $\tan^2 A = \dfrac{\sin^2 A}{\cos^2 A}$]

PRACTICE PAPER B

Paper 1

1 (*a*) (i) £4500 (ii) £3000, £5200 (iii) £1100 (*b*) $\dfrac{8}{25}$

2 $3x^3 + 8x^2 + 3x - 2$ 3 (*a*) $(4x - 3y)(4x + 3y)$ (*b*) $(x - 4)(x + 7)$

4 $p = 3$

5 (*a*)   (*b*) symmetric

(*c*) 48 (The manufacturer might wish to quote a lower average for trade descriptions reasons.)

6 (*a*) 16   (*b*) 4   7 $t = \pm\sqrt{\dfrac{v + w}{3}}$ 8 (*a*) $4\sqrt{3}$ (*b*) $\dfrac{2 - x}{x(x + 1)}$

9 (*a*) collecting his pension
(*b*) on a Saturday when Raith Rovers are not playing at home   (*c*) 4

PRACTICE PAPER B

Paper 2

1 (*a*) 53, 6·36   (*b*) The women are younger on average with a similar spread of ages.

2 1·79   3 Premier $(2160 > 2153·78)$

4 (*a*) $5x + 4y = 128$ (*b*) $3x + 2y = 76·5$ (*c*) £25 per day; 75p per litre

5 £491·71   6 (*a*) $(3, 16)$ (*b*) $(0, 7)$ (*c*) $(-1, 0)$

7 (*a*) 64 000 cm³   (*b*) 972   8 305 miles   9 (*a*) $a^2 + 2a^{-\frac{1}{2}}$ (*b*) $-2·1, 0·8$

10 (*a*) £5580·24   (*b*) £663·36   11 $k = -30$ 12 111·3 cm

13 (*a*) 221·8, 318·2   (*b*) proof [Use $\tan A = \dfrac{\sin A}{\cos A}$]   14 27

PRACTICE PAPER C

Paper 1

1 (a)

goals	freq	cum f
0	2	2
1	2	4
2	5	9
3	5	14
4	4	18
5	1	19
6	1	20
11	2	22

(b) $\dfrac{5}{11}$

2 (a) $8k^2 + 17k - 3$

(b) (i) $4y(2y - 1)$

    (ii) $(x - 10)(x + 10)$

3 (a) $Q_2 = 2, Q_1 = 1, Q_3 = 4$

(b)

(c) (i) The lower club median suggests that the boys were late for school more often than the youth club.

    (ii) The validity is questionable because:
- The school sample is 5 times as large as the club sample.
- It is unfair to compare a compulsory morning activity with a voluntary evening activity.

4 (a) $(-3, 4)$ (b) $x = -3$ (c) 4   **5** (a) 8   (b) 32

6 (a) $3\sqrt{7}$ (b) $\dfrac{x - 1}{x^2}$ **7** $(2x - 3)(3x - 2)$

8 (a) £10,900   (b) No (since $575 < 600$).

PRACTICE PAPER C

Paper 2

1 (a) 12; 1·79   (b) similar spread, John has more plums => John's plums are smaller

2 $\dfrac{3}{5}$ **3** $d = 5$ **4** in the son's 5th year of employment

5 $x = 5, y = -3$ **6** 11 600 mm^3 **7** no ($4·7 > 4$)

8 (a) $2x$ (b) $v = \pm \dfrac{\sqrt{x - 3u}}{2}$ **9** the bank loan ($2340 < 2458·40$)

10 5·79 m^2 **11** $y = 4 - x^2$ **12** (a) £19, 540   (b) £2973·20

13 69·2°   **14** $-1·43, 0·18$ **15** (a) 8·94 cm   (b) 30, 150

16 60

PRACTICE PAPER D

Paper 1

1 (a)

age	freq	cum f
11	7	7
12	8	15
13	6	21
14	5	26
15	3	29

(b) 12

2 (a) $2p^2 + 3pq$ (b) $a(x + y + 2)$

3 60°   **4** 135, 315

5 $-3, \dfrac{1}{2}$

6 (a) $q + 1000p = 30$ (b) $q + 1600p = 39$ (c) £15 per quarter, $1\frac{1}{2}$p per unit

7 (a) about 27   (b) Yes, 80% responded to in under 13 minutes
or 56 responded to in under 15 minutes.

8

9 $8\dfrac{2}{3}$ **10** (a) $4\sqrt{5}$ (b) $\dfrac{5}{9}$

11 £149·63

PRACTICE PAPER D

Paper 2

1 $(5 - 2k)(5 + 2k)$ **2** 5 cm

3 (a) H1 H2 H3 H4 H5 H6   (b) (ii) $\{\dfrac{4}{12} > \dfrac{3}{12}\}$ **4** £18·55
T1 T2 T3 T4 T5 T6

5 94 cm³   **6** $a = \dfrac{2A - bh}{h}$ **7** 181 cm²   **8** £503·50

9 $k = 2$ **10** 2512·8 m²   **11** (a) x^2 (b) $\dfrac{3\sqrt{5}}{5}$

12 (a) £29,104   (b) £6239·20

13 (a) $y = 16 - \dfrac{3}{4}x$ (b) 13   (c) Reasonably confident (most points close to regression line).
[some variation in these answers is acceptable]

14 70·5, 289·5   **15** 17·4   **16** 1·42 m

17 (a) $\dfrac{x + 1}{x^2}$ (b) $\dfrac{2x + 1}{x^2}$

PRACTICE PAPER E

Paper 1

1   (*a*)   44, 7

2 $y = \dfrac{1}{2}x + 2$ **3** $(6x - 7y)(6x + 7y)$

4   0·174   **5** $(x + 1)(x - 3)$

6   (2, 3)

7   (*a*) $(2x + 3)^2$ (*b*) $\dfrac{3x + 2y}{xy}$ (*c*) $t = \dfrac{m - r}{k}$

8   (*a*) $57\dfrac{1}{3}$ (*b*)   1

9   (*a*) $4x^{\frac{4}{3}}$ (*b*) $3(\sqrt{5} - 2)$ **10**   £59

(*b*)

x	freq	cum f
30	2	2
35	1	3
36	3	6
37	1	7
41	4	11
43	1	12
45	1	13
47	3	16
48	1	17
50	1	18
51	1	19
52	2	21
53	3	24

PRACTICE PAPER E

Paper 2

1   (*a*)   2·61   (*b*) $\dfrac{1}{3}$ **2** $y = \dfrac{2}{3}x + 3$ **3**   15 cm

4   (*a*) $3k(k - 3)$ (*b*) $x^3 - 5x^2 + 10x - 8$ **5**   after 4 years (i.e. in the fifth)

6   1247 m²

7   (*a*)   For 4 or 8 pages Quickprint is cheaper than Rapidprint and for 12 or more pages
              Quickprint is more expensive than Rapidprint.
      (*b*)   For 4, 8, 12 pages use Fastprint. For 16 or more use Rapidprint.

8   (*a*)   (3, −1)   (*b*)   (6, 8)   (*c*)   T (2, 0)   U (4, 0)

9   (*a*)   £2305   (*b*)   £1644·96   **10**   34·9 cm   **11**   80·6 cm

12   (*a*)   £6699·24   (*b*)   £38·16   (*c*)   The APR is less for the larger loan.

13   (*a*) $-1, \dfrac{2}{3}$ (*b*) $9\sqrt{2}$ (*c*)   48·2, 311·8   **14**   2·34

PRACTICE PAPER F

Paper 1

1 (a) $x^3 - x^2 + 4x - 4$ (b) $(5p - 3q)(5p + 3q)$ **2**

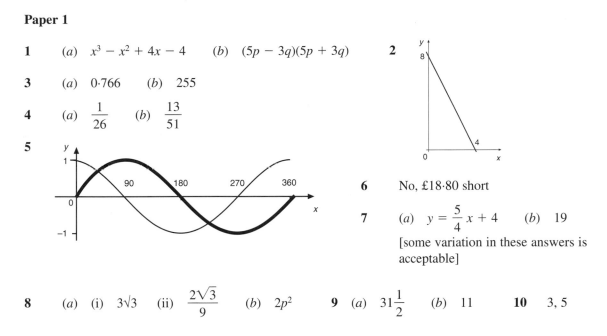

3 (a) 0·766   (b) 255

4 (a) $\dfrac{1}{26}$ (b) $\dfrac{13}{51}$

5

6 No, £18·80 short

7 (a) $y = \dfrac{5}{4}x + 4$ (b) 19
[some variation in these answers is acceptable]

8 (a) (i) $3\sqrt{3}$ (ii) $\dfrac{2\sqrt{3}}{9}$ (b) $2p^2$ **9** (a) $31\dfrac{1}{2}$ (b) 11   **10** 3, 5

PRACTICE PAPER F

Paper 2

1 (a) $Q_2 = 126$ $Q_1 = 124$ $Q_3 = 127$ (b) Yes, median > 125

(c)

123 124 125 126 127 128 129

(d) Queen's Hotel (same median but less spread than the Royal below the median; and more spread above median)

2 8 cm   **3** £32·50   **4** $y = 2x + 9$

5 (a) $7x + 5y = 225$ (b) $5x + 4y = 165$ (c) £25 per day, £10 per 100 miles

6 77 124 cm^3 **7** (a) (2, 1)   (b) $a = -2, b = 1$ **8** 29·0°

9 (a) £10,500   (b) £1161·50   **10** (a) 36·9364   (b) 36·33   (c) 1·6%

11 $(2x + 1)(x - 2)$ **12** $r = \dfrac{pq}{4}$ **13** 143·1, 323·1

14 (a) (i) $\dfrac{1}{x}$ (ii) $\dfrac{3}{x - 2}$ (b) $\dfrac{2(2x - 1)}{x(x - 2)}$ **15** (a) 180   (b) 1080   (c) 45

16 £8075   **17** 89·4 seconds

QUESTION FREQUENCY CHART

PRACTICE PAPER	A1	A2	B1	B2	C1	C2	D1	D2	E1	E2	F1	F2
percentages, apprecn/deprecn		4		3		4		4		5		3, 10
volume (sphere, cone, prism)		10		7		6	5					6
gradient formula						2						
$y = mx + c$ (given equn, find m, c)	1a										2	
$y = mx + c$ (from graph)	1b								2	2		4
simple expanding brackets					2a		2a				1a	
harder expanding brackets (*)		2	2							4b		
common factors		3a			2b(i)		2b			4a		
simple difference of two squares					2b(ii)							
harder difference of two squares (*)			3a					1	3		1b	
factorising trinomials ($a = 1$)		3b	3b						5			
factorising trinomials ($a > 1$) (*)					7							11
length of arc		12		12	13					10		
area of sector								10				
tangent & radius; angle in semicircle	3						3			3		2
centre, chord, perp. bisector (*)				2		3		2				
trig angles > 90		9					4		4		3	
0.5 absinC						10		7		6		
sine rule						7		16				
cosine rule (for a side)		15		8						11		
cosine rule (for an angle) (*)												8
construct a formula		6		4a, b			6a, b					5a, b
significance of intersection of graphs										7		
simultaneous equations		5		4c		5	6c		6			5c
make pie chart, box plot, dot plot	6c, d		5		3b, c							1c, d
cum. frequency	2a				1a		1a		1b			
median + quartiles	6a, b		1a		3a		1b		1a			1a, b
standard deviation		1		1	1					1a		
best fitting line (regression)								13			7	
probability	2b		1b		1b			3		1b	4	
simplify algebraic fractions								17	7a			14a
4 rules for algebraic fractions	8c		8b		6b			17	7b			14b
change of subject of formula		11a	7			8b		6	7c			12
simplify surds			8a		6a		10a			13b		
rationalise simple denominators	8b							11b			8a	
rationalise compound denominators (*)									9b			
indices	8a			9a		8a	10b	11a	9a		8b	
recognise quadratic graphs	7					11		9				
turning point, axis of symmetry		13		6	4					8		7
quadratic equns (by factors)							5			13a	10	
quadratic equns (by formula)		11b		9b	14							
trig graphs (e.g. 2sin 3x)	4		4				8					
trig graphs (e.g. cos ($x + 30$)) (*)				11							5	
trig equations		17a		13a		15		14		13c		13
periodicity		7										15
identities (*)		17b		13b								
wages & salaries	5	8				12a	8			9	6	9a
tax		8		5		12b	12					9b
loans				10		9				12		
networks & flowcharts	9		9		8		11		10			16
formulae		14	6		5		9		8		9	
statistics		16		14		16	7	15		14		17

(*) The topics marked with an asterisk are of a greater level of difficulty

FORMULAE LIST

The roots of $ax^2 + bx + c = 0$ are $x = \dfrac{-b \pm \sqrt{(b^2 - 4ac)}}{2a}$.

Sine rule: $\quad \dfrac{a}{\sin A} = \dfrac{b}{\sin B} = \dfrac{c}{\sin C}$

Cosine rule: $\quad a^2 = b^2 + c^2 - 2bc \cos A \quad$ or $\quad \cos A = \dfrac{b^2 + c^2 - a^2}{2bc}$

Area of a triangle: $\quad \dfrac{1}{2} ab \sin C$

Volume of a sphere: $\quad \dfrac{4}{3} \pi r^3$

Volume of a cone: $\quad \dfrac{1}{3} \pi r^2 h$

Volume of a cylinder: $\quad \pi r^2 h$

Standard deviation:
where n is the sample size. $\quad \sqrt{\dfrac{\Sigma(x - \bar{x})^2}{n - 1}} = \sqrt{\dfrac{\Sigma x^2 - \dfrac{(\Sigma x)^2}{n}}{n - 1}}$